Supers
and the
Crazy Rain Maker

Russell Punter

Illustrated by Josh Cleland

Contents

The Animal Action Squad

The **Animal Action Squad** is a top secret organization of superheroes dedicated to fighting crime.

In this story, you'll be working alongside **Supersquirrel** to defeat an evil genius.

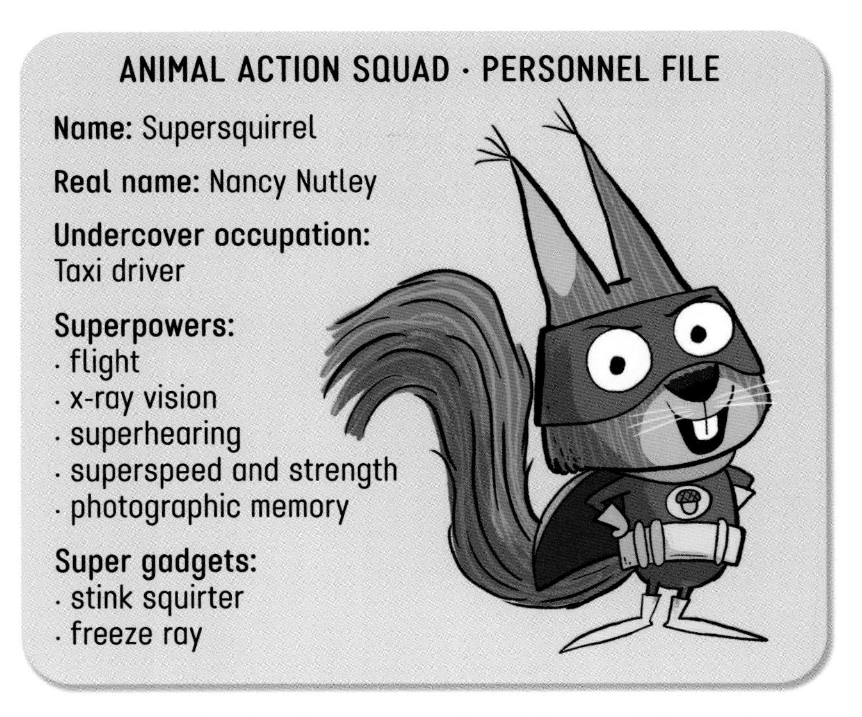

You can help Supersquirrel by solving the puzzles that appear throughout this book.

Look at the pictures carefully and watch out for clues all the time.

There are extra clues on pages 74-75 and you can check the answers on pages 76-79. Don't worry if you can't solve every puzzle – some are trickier than others!

Supersquirrel will need all the help you can give her to outwit fiendish criminal mastermind **Dr. Drizzle** and his sidekick **Rocky**. Keep an eye out for them!

Briefing complete. Turn the page to begin your Animal Action Squad mission...

Catnapped

It was a busy morning on the streets of Fleaville. Taxi driver Nancy Nutley (secret identity: Supersquirrel) had just dropped off a passenger when...

…she spotted a tough-looking dog bundling a small, elderly cat into a car.

"HELP!" came a cry. "I'm being catnapped!"

As the car roared off, Nancy gave chase. She'd only seen the cat for a split second, but he looked familiar.

Time for one of her superpowers – her photographic memory.

As she flicked through the images in her mind, she knew EXACTLY who he was!

Do you?

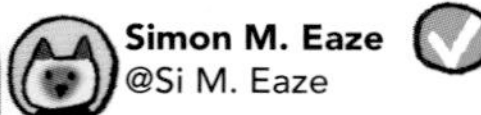

Simon M. Eaze
@Si M. Eaze

Just joined Twitcher today! This is my first Twitch. #sihasarrived

FELINE ONLINE HEADLINES

Weather expert Professor Max Manx has arrived in Fleaville to give a speech about his new discovery. He is staying at the Pawchester Hotel.

THE DAILY MEWS

A PURR-FECT FIT

Reporter: Kitty Litter

Former Meowchester United soccer star, Fred Furball, launched his new range of sportswear yesterday at Fleaman's Department Store.

BREAKING NEWS... Len Lynx sets 100m record

The chase is on

The catnapper seemed to be heading for the docks. Nancy checked her supermemory for a road plan. There was only one clear route. **Can you find it?**

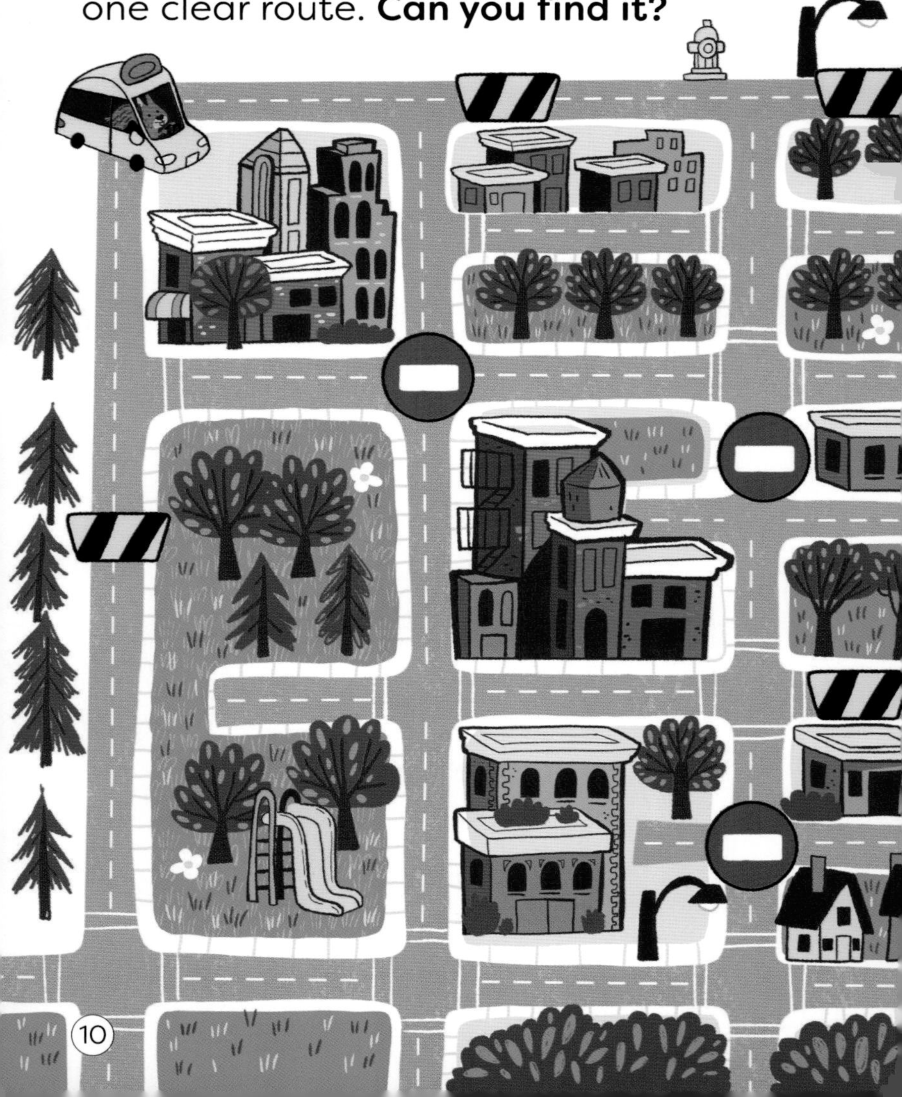

ONE WAY
ONE WAY
ONE WAY
ONE WAY
DOCKS

The missing Professor

KA-BOOM!
Supersquirrel!
Supersquirrel races inside...
Where are they?

Just then, there was a muffled cry from a room nearby. But which one?

"I'll use my x-ray vision to look through the walls," thought Supersquirrel.

Which room is the Professor in?

Island dilemma

WHHIRRR!
So long, caped chump!
But Rocky hasn't counted on Supersquirrel's amazing powers...
WHOOSH!
Rats!

Supersquirrel's speed is no match for Rocky...
You won't get away!

She has almost caught up, when...
Try some of my engine oil, Nutty!
SQUIRT!
Urrggh!

By the time Supersquirrel could see again, Rocky had vanished. “He must have landed on one of the islands below,” she thought.

She checked her supermemory for information. Only one island was safe.

MAPFAX

8 Leg Island

Home to deadly, poisonous giant **spiders**.

MAPFAX

Lava Island

The **volcano** here could erupt at any moment.

MAPFAX

Slime Island

The slimy **seaweed** here is fatal to touch.

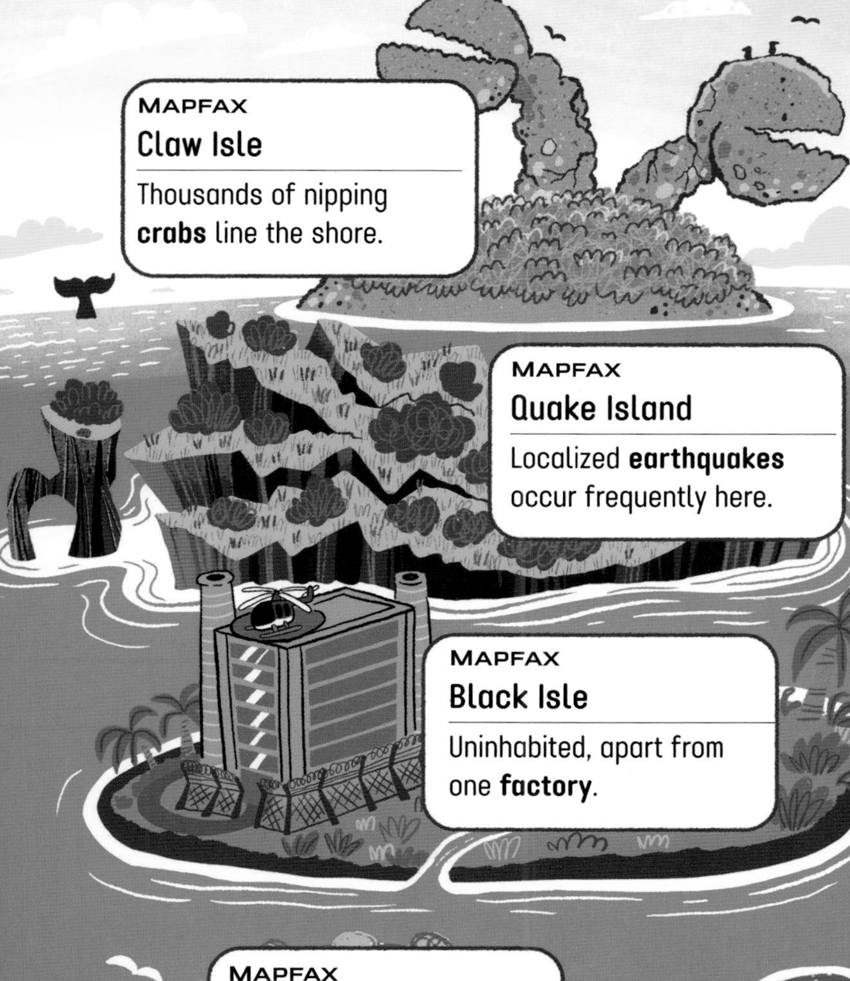

Which island is safe?

Break in

Supersquirrel landed a short distance from the factory and silently crept closer.

"Rocky must have taken the Professor inside," she thought. "It doesn't look very friendly. I'll have to find a way in, without being seen."

Can you see Supersquirrel's only way into the factory?

NO ENTRY
without full
security
clearance.
THIS MEANS
YOU!

Undercover

With Supersquirrel inside at last...
I just hope Professor Manx is okay.

Workers' uniforms!

Now I can snoop around without being noticed.

Where has she seen the name before?

Inside the factory

Where is the Professor being held?

Locked up

Supersquirrel soon found herself outside a door marked **TOP SECRET**. From inside, she heard a muffled voice she recognized – the Professor!

"Time to put my x-ray vision and superhearing into action," she thought.

There was the Professor – with Rocky and a mean-looking silver cat in a suit. Professor Manx was mixing some chemicals.

"Hurry up, Professor," snarled the silver cat. "I need your secret formula NOW! No one keeps Darius Drizzle waiting."

Here it is, Dr. Drizzle. But what do you want it for?
You'll see soon enough.

May I go home now?
Not until my plan is complete.

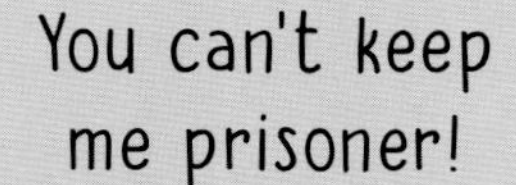
You can't keep me prisoner!

Wanna bet?

Supersquirrel will rescue me!
Who?

Some flying fool came after us, Boss. But I lost her.
RING!

What is it?
Floor Eight here. The equipment is ready for inspection, sir!

Excellent. I'll bring you the formula.
Mass production can begin immediately.

Lock the lab door behind us, Rocky. You remember the code?
Yes Boss, it's the same as the code to open it...

What is the 6-digit code?

The secret of Floor Eight

A harmless chemical. But spray it into clouds and it makes rain.
Amazing!

Yes, no more droughts and lots of healthy plants.
Hmm. Something tells me Dr. Drizzle isn't interested in saving the planet.

Stealthily, Supersquirrel and the Professor made their way to the eighth floor.

"Wow, look at that!" gasped Supersquirrel. Zooming along below them was a massive production line of...

"**Drones!**" said Professor Manx. "Hundreds of them."

"But Drizzle makes rainwear..." wondered Supersquirrel. "Why does he need drones?"

"Where is he, by the way?" whispered the Professor.

Supersquirrel's supersight spotted Dr. Drizzle instantly. **Can you see him?**

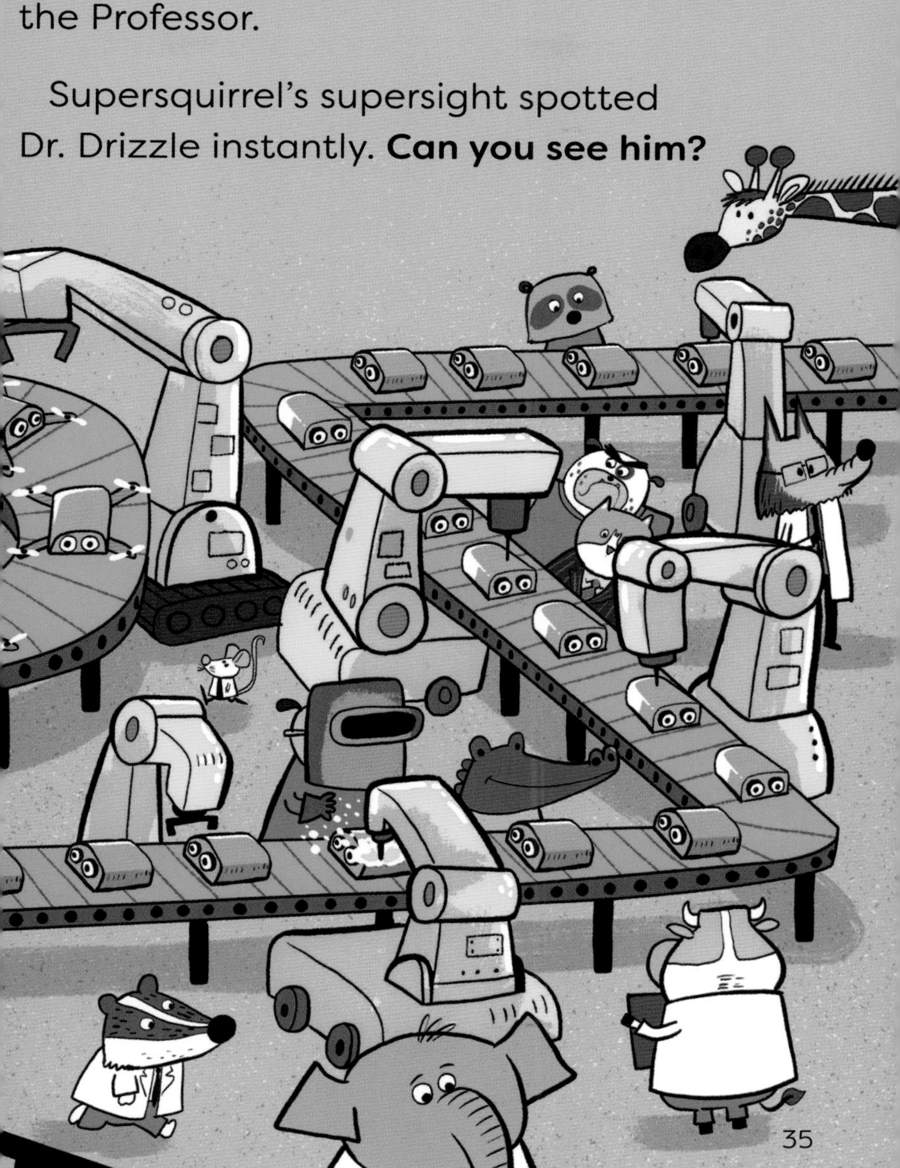

Code names

Dr. Drizzle approaches a technician...
Start downloading the instructions to the drones.
Yes, sir.

They're programming the drones.
To do what? Hide here while I find out.

Supersquirrel sneaks behind the technician...
A quick squirt of my stink spray should do the trick...
SQUIRT!
Pooh! What's the awful smell?
Eww! It's worse than stinky feet!
You need to shower – and fast!
Get cleaned up and hurry back!

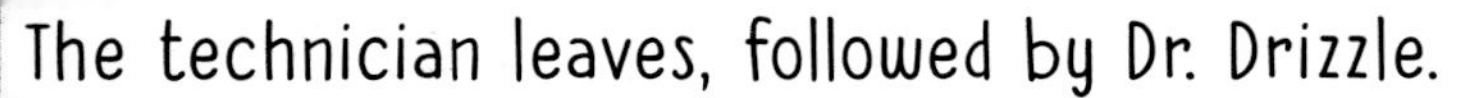
The technician leaves, followed by Dr. Drizzle.

Ha, ha! My plan worked. Now to check out that computer...
Hmmm. The folder names are all in code.
I may not have time to open them *all* and memorize the contents.
REMIT
DEEPS
SEKARB
NALPTHGILF
YRETTAB
ELGNA
LORTNOCTEJ
SLACIMEHC
ROTOMROTOR

Can you see a Flight Plan folder?

Which way out?

It only took Supersquirrel a split second to memorize the computer code in the folder. Next moment, she heard a cry behind her.

"There's Supersquirrel! Grab her!"

It was Rocky. In a flash, Supersquirrel ran back to the Professor. "Time to get out of here!" she yelled, as an alarm rang out.

They raced through the nearest exit, with Rocky close behind.

"If we head to the roof, I can fly us away," cried Supersquirrel.

There were eight doors in front of them. Supersquirrel thought back to when she first entered the factory. She knew which door led to the roof. **Do you?**

Trapped

As Supersquirrel goes to open the door...
Going somewhere?
Dr. Drizzle!
K.O. SQUIRTER

This may look like a water squirter, but it contains knock-out fluid.
Whew! You got them, Boss.
K.O. SQUIRTER

So you're the great Supersquirrel, here to rescue the Professor.
She nearly did, too!
K.O. SQUIRTER

Just what are you up to, Drizzle?
I'll tell you. The information won't do you any good now...
K.O. SQUIRTER

On my production line are over a hundred drones.

At this moment, they're being filled with the Professor's wonderful rain-making chemical.

The drones will fly above Fleaville...

...and spray the chemical into the clouds.

This will make it rain... and rain... and rain...

In fact, it will rain non-stop, until the authorities agree to hand over the contents of the National Bank.

Either they agree, or Fleaville ends up underwater...

...which should do wonders for the sales of my rain gear! Either way, I'll make a fortune. Meow-ha-ha!

Dr. Drizzle marched them to his office.

"The drones have just taken off," he purred. "The on-board cameras will give us a splendid view. How long till they reach Fleaville, Rocky?"

"Um, I'm not sure, Boss," he replied. "They fly at 100 miles per hour and Fleaville is exactly 10 miles away."

It only took Supersquirrel a second to calculate how little time she had left to stop the drones.

What time will the drones arrive in Fleaville?

TIME NOW: 3:10 p.m.
K.O. SQUIRTER

Downpour

The drones swoop over Fleaville...
WHOOSH!
What *are* they?
What's going on?
SPRAY!
SPRAY!
SPRAY!

Minutes later...
Help!
I'm drenched!
Take cover!

Back on Black Isle, Dr. Drizzle was delighted.

"Ha, ha!" he cackled. "My plan's working!"

"You've twisted my wonderful discovery," wailed the Professor.

"You'll never get away with this," fumed Supersquirrel.

"Button it, Nutty!" bawled Rocky.

Dr. Drizzle switched on the TV news, but the freak weather had messed up the signal.

Can you match the speech with the pictures?

...students have been evacuated...
BREAKING NEWS
FTV

...the Fleaville Fun Fair is a washout...
BREAKING NEWS
FTV

This chart shows more than a month's rain has fallen in the last hour.
SCHOOL BUS
BREAKING NEWS
FTV

...farmers' fields are flooded...
BREAKING NEWS
FTV

...all sports games have been called off...
BREAKING NEWS
FTV

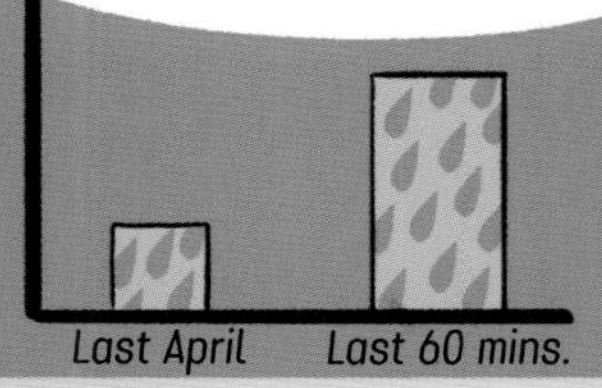
...emergency services can't cope...
Last April
Last 60 mins.
BREAKING NEWS
FTV

Escape

Now to issue my demands...
CLICK!
Citizens of Fleaville – this is Dr. Drizzle!
Hand over all the money in the National Bank, or I'll drown the city!

While Dr. Drizzle and Rocky are distracted...
Run for it, Professor!
STOP THEM!
K.O. SQUIRTER
Try my freeze ray for size, Rocky!
K.O. SQUIRTER
FRE-E-E-ZE!

Rats! She's frozen the knock-out fluid.
K.O. SQUIRTER

Outside the office...
We need something to jam these doors!

Ah, I think I see what we can use.
CLEANING IN PROGRESS. BACK IN 10 MINUTES.

Can you?

Code breaker

When they arrive...
We're in luck. There's no one around.
What's your idea?
FOLDER LOCKED
We find the flight plan on this computer and reprogram the drones.
Drat! They've locked the folder.

Never mind. I memorized the flight plan code...
I'll just type it in again.
FLEX!
Supersquirrel types at superspeed...
DRONEFLIGHTPLANONE
PROCEEDTOCOORDINAT
ESSIXONESIXTOSIXON
ETWOOVERFLEAVILLEA
NDSPREADO
Amazing!
TAP!
TAP!
TAP!
TAP!
Seconds later...
Now I just need to replace the word FLEAVILLE with BLACK ISLE.

Can you find the word FLEAVILLE in the program code? It appears four times.

D R O N E F L I G H T P L A N O N E

P R O C E E D T O C O O R D I N A T

E S S I X O N E S I X T O S I X O N

E T W O O V E R F L E A V I L L E A

N D S P R E A D O U T O P E N V E N

T S P R A Y D R O N E F L I G H T P

L A N T W O P R O C E E D T O C O O

R D I N A T E S T W O O N E N I N E

O V E R F L E A V I L L E A N D S P

R E A D O U T O P E N V E N T S P R

A Y D R O N E F L I G H T P L A N T

H R E E P R O C E E D T O C O O R D

I N A T E S N I N E O N E T O T H R

E E F O U R S E V E N T E E N O V E

R F L E A V I L L E A N D S P R E A

D O U T O P E N V E N T S P R A Y M

A I N T A I N F I N A L P O S I T I

O N O V E R F L E A V I L L E E N D

Chute out

Supersquirrel has just finished when...
Step away from the computer, Nutty!
Quick! Down here, it's our only chance.
REFUSE CHUTE to Floor 2

What will happen in six minutes' time?

On the run

Supersquirrel and the Professor ran from floor to floor, avoiding Dr. Drizzle, Rocky and the staff, until they reached the roof.

Can you see the route they took?

FIRE ESCAPE to
ROOF/FLOOR 7
STAIRS
FIRE ESCAPE to
ROOF/FLOOR 8
ELEVATOR
to Floor 5
ELEVATOR
to Floor 6
STAIRS
STAIRS
ELEVATOR to
Floor 2
STAIRS
ELEVATOR to
Floor 3

Washout

Before Supersquirrel can fly them to freedom, they're grabbed by guards...
Gotcha!
You can't escape now.
But then...
Look!
It's the drones!
What?!

SPRAY!
SPRAY!
SPRAY!
Oh no!
Help!
They'll flood the island!
Don't panic! That's an order!

Outside the factory, Drizzle's workers run, as the river bursts its banks...
Help!
Quick, get inside the factory!
The staff rush to the safety of the roof, as the water climbs higher...

...and higher...
...and higher...
It's over, Drizzle!
Curse you, Supersquirrel!

Dr. Drizzle runs to his private helicopter...
Wait for me, boss!
They're getting away!
We'll stop them. Hold on tight, Professor!

They won't get far!

Which dial seems to be showing the wrong information?

Drizzle dries off

And so...
FLEAVILLE PRISON
GOVERNOR: WILLY WOOF
Scuppered by a squirrel! I'll never live it down.
I'll arrange a clean-up operation on Black Isle.
I'll fly you to your hotel, Professor.
Thanks, Supersquirrel – for everything!

The next morning...

THE FLEAVILLE TIMES

Wednesday 7th April

Today's weather: Becoming dry

RAINSTORM SPECIAL EDITION

Supersquirrel foils downpour plot

Rain gear tycoon's plan to drown the city ends in failure

Bob Tail
Chief reporter

Dr. Darius Drizzle and his assistant Rocky are now behind bars after Supersquirrel stopped their fiendish schemes. Drizzle used an army of drones to create non-stop rain over the city, causing chaos. Luckily, Supersquirrel, assisted by Professor Max Manx, reprogrammed the drones and saved Fleaville from disaster. Drizzle's staff were later airlifted from the roof of his factory on Black Isle. All the drones have been collected by the police. No one knows Supersquirrel's true identity, but whoever she is, the citizens of Fleaville are in her debt.

Supersquirrel

Drizzle and Rocky are now in Fleaville Prison

Manx speech goes ahead

Pawline Pooch
Science reporter

Professor Max Manx, who was catnapped by Dr. Drizzle, will make a speech at the Corgi Conference Hall at 11 a.m. today. He will explain how his rain-making discovery works.

Professor Max Manx

SPORTS - Fleaville Rovers game flooded out - Page 44

Where does the Professor want to go?

Clues

Page 8
Look at the Feline Online story.

Pages 10-11
Start by going straight ahead, take the first road on Nancy's right, then the next left.

Page 14
Look out for an item of clothing worn by the Professor.

Pages 18-19
Only one island has no hazards.

Pages 20-21
Examine the fence closely.

Page 23
Look back at the picture on page 7.

Page 25
Look back at the sign on page 23.

Page 31
A leap year has one more day than a normal year.

Pages 34-35
Dr. Drizzle is somewhere on page 35.

Page 39
REMIT = TIMER.

Pages 40-41
Look back at the sign on page 23.

Page 46
It will take 60 minutes divided by ten.

Pages 50-51
The emergency service is a fire truck. The students are in a yellow bus.

Page 55
Which long item would fit between the door handles?

Page 59
The word is on rows 4, 9, 15 and 18.

Page 61
What has Supersquirrel done on page 58?

Pages 62-63
To get started, take the first two sets of stairs you come to.

Page 69
If the helicopter is moving, which dial would be incorrect?

Page 73
Read the newspaper on page 72.

Answers

Page 8

The cat pictured in the Feline Online story is the same one Supersquirrel saw on page 6.

Pages 10-11

The route is marked in black.

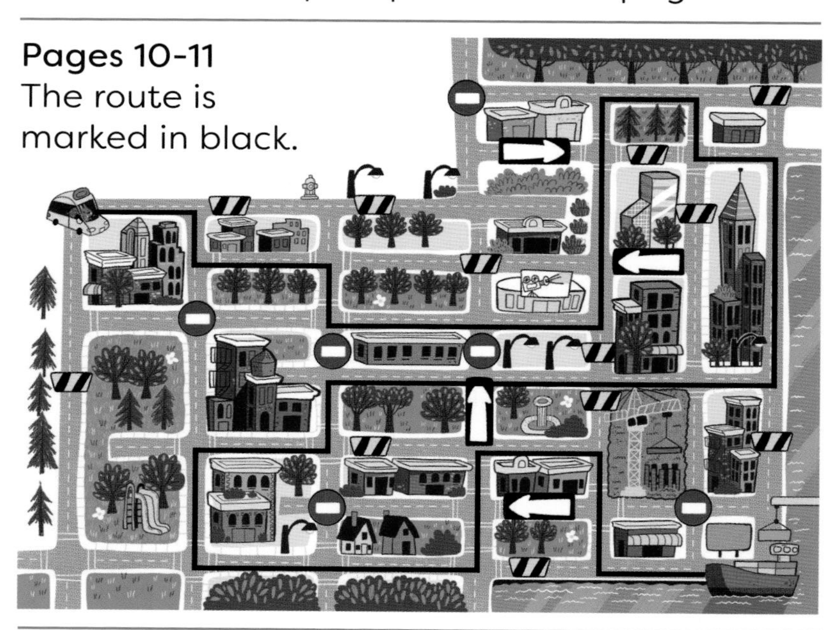

Page 14

The Professor is in the Loading Bay. You can see his scarf.

Pages 18-19

Black Isle is the safest place to land.

Pages 20-21
Supersquirrel can get through the hole in the fence, then the open side door. (The guard is snoozing and the security camera is broken.)

Page 23
Supersquirrel saw the name **Drizzle Industries** on the poster on page 7.

Page 25
The Professor is in the Laboratory, which is on the floor above the canteen (see the sign on page 23).

Page 31
The code is 7 1 2 3 6 6. (7 days in a week, 12 months in a year, 366 days in a leap year.)

Pages 34-35
Dr. Drizzle is circled in yellow.

Page 39
The file names are all written backwards. So NALPTHGILF = FLIGHTPLAN.

Pages 40-41
The green door leads to the roof. Each floor is coded, as shown on the sign on page 23.

Page 46

The drones will arrive at 3:16 p.m. The clock shows it's currently 3:10 p.m. The drones travel at 100 miles per hour, so to travel 10 miles will take one tenth of 60 minutes = 6 minutes.

Pages 50-51

Here are the correct matches.

Page 55

Sliding the mop handle between the door handles will stop the doors from opening.

Page 59

Fleaville is hidden here:

D R O N E F L I G H T P L A N O N E
P R O C E E D T O C O O R D I N A T
E S S I X O N E S I X T O S I X O N
E T W O O V E R F L E A V I L L E A
N D S P R E A D O U T O P E N V E N
T S P R A Y D R O N E F L I G H T P
L A N T W O P R O C E E D T O C O O
R D I N A T E S T W O O N E N I N E
O V E R F L E A V I L L E A N D S P
R E A D O U T O P E N V E N T S P R
A Y D R O N E F L I G H T P L A N T
H R E E P R O C E E D T O C O O R D
I N A T E S N I N E O N E T O T H R
E E F O U R S E V E N T E E N O V E
R F L E A V I L L E A N D S P R E A
D O U T O P E N V E N T S P R A Y M
A I N T A I N F I N A L P O S I T I
O N O V E R F L E A V I L L E E N D

Page 61

Supersquirrel has reprogrammed the drones to return to Black Isle. It will take them six minutes to arrive (see page 46).

Pages 62-63

Their route is marked in black.

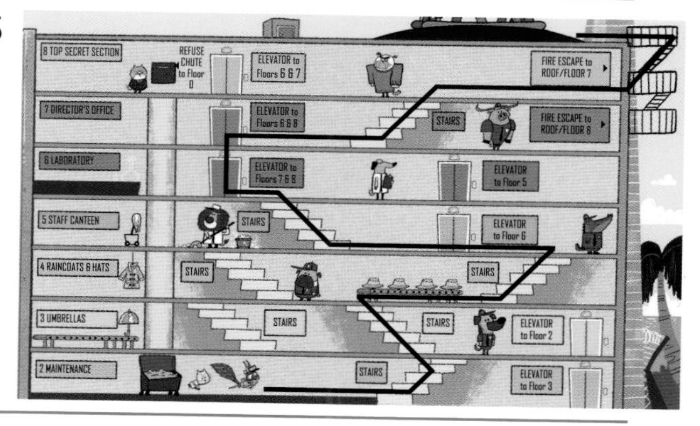

Page 69

The Helicopter Speed dial is showing zero. Dr. Drizzle thinks the helicopter should be moving, so this seems wrong to him.

Page 73

The Professor is going to the Corgi Conference Hall. This is mentioned in the newspaper article on page 72.

Ready for your next mission?

Look out for more adventures with the **Animal Action Squad**. Which superhero will you help next?

Series editor: Lesley Sims

First published in 2024 by Usborne Publishing Limited, 83-85 Saffron Hill, London EC1N 8RT, United Kingdom. usborne.com